No Two Alike

Description

Students explore the phenomenon that although bird species can be identified by certain traits, no two birds are *exactly* alike. After a read-aloud about bird watching, students set up a bird feeder station so they can observe local birds. They use a poster to identify the birds they see, read an article about similarities and differences within bird species, and listen to a story about two birds that are almost, but not quite, the same. Finally, they create a "spot the difference" picture showing two birds of the same species that are almost identical but have a slight variation in traits.

Alignment With the *Next Generation Science Standards*

Performance Expectation		
1-LS3-1: Make observations to construct an evidence-based account that young plants and animals are like, but not exactly like, their parents.		
Science and Engineering Practices	**Disciplinary Core Idea**	**Crosscutting Concept**
Asking Questions and Defining Problems Ask questions based on observations to find more information about the natural and/or designed world(s). **Planning and Carrying Out Investigations** Make observations (firsthand and from media) and/or measurements to collect data that can be used to make comparisons. **Obtaining, Evaluating, and Communicating Information** Obtain information using various texts, text features, and other media that will be useful in answering a scientific question and/or supporting a scientific claim.	**LS3.B: Variation of Traits** Individuals of the same kind of plant or animal are recognizable as similar but can also vary in many ways.	**Patterns** Patterns in the natural world can be observed, used to describe phenomena, and used as evidence.

Note: The activities in this lesson will help students move toward the performance expectations listed, which is the goal after multiple activities. However, the activities will not by themselves be sufficient to reach the performance expectations.

Featured Picture Books

TITLE: *Ruby's Birds*
AUTHOR: **Mya Thompson**
ILLUSTRATOR: **Claudia Dávila**
PUBLISHER: **The Cornell Lab Publishing Group**
YEAR: **2019**
GENRE: **Story**
SUMMARY: *Ruby lives in New York City and loves to sing and make noise. Her neighbor takes her birding in Central Park where Ruby learns that you must be still and quiet to watch the birds. Finally, Ruby takes her own family to Central Park and teaches them how to birdwatch.*

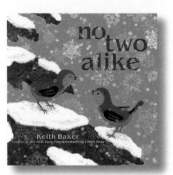

TITLE: *No Two Alike*
AUTHOR: **Keith Baker**
ILLUSTRATOR: **Keith Baker**
PUBLISHER: **Beach Lane**
YEAR: **2011**
GENRE: **Poetry**
SUMMARY: *Through playful rhyme and whimsical illustrations, we follow two birds on a snowy day who point out how no two snowflakes, nests, leaves, branches, and so forth are exactly alike.*

Time Needed

This lesson will take several class periods. Suggested scheduling is as follows:

Session 1: **Engage** with *Ruby's Birds* Read-Aloud and Set Up a Feeder Station

Session 2: **Explore** with Analyzing Bird ID Charts and FeederWatch

Session 3: **Explain** with Birds of a Feather Article

Session 4: **Elaborate** with *No Two Alike* Read-Aloud

Session 5: **Evaluate** with Spot the Difference Challenge

Materials

For FeederWatch (per class)

- A variety of bird feeders and/or items for students to make bird feeders
- Different types of feed
- *Optional:* Baby monitor for listening to bird sounds outside the classroom
- Posters of common feeder birds (see the "Websites" section at the end of this lesson)

NOTE: You will need an outdoor area for the bird feeders.

National Science Teaching Association

For Spot the Difference Challenge

- Crayons or colored pencils

Student Pages

- Birds of a Feather
- Spot the Difference Challenge
- STEM Everywhere

Background for Teachers

Birds are our most visible wildlife neighbors. No matter if you live in the city, the suburbs, or a rural area, there are bound to be birds around. The core idea addressed in this lesson is about variation of traits in living things: specifically, the phenomenon that individuals of the same species are recognizable as similar but can also vary in many ways. Birds are an excellent subject for this concept, because it is fairly easy to identify bird species based on their observable traits, there are slight differences between individuals of a species, and birds are animals that most students can directly observe.

There is much diversity in appearance and behaviors of birds, from the ostrich that can grow up to 9 feet tall and weigh 280 pounds, to the tiny bee hummingbird that is only 2 ¼ inches long and weighs almost as much as a dime, and thousands in between. Most birds fly, but some, like ostriches and penguins, cannot. Some birds are expert swimmers. Birds come in a wide variety of sizes and shapes, and in just about every color of the rainbow. A 2016 study from the American Museum of Natural History estimates that there are about 18,000 species of birds on Earth (Barrowclough et al. 2016). Although there is a wide diversity of bird species, there are certain things all birds have in common. These are the characteristics that make a bird a *bird*. All birds have wings, feathers, bills (beaks), two legs, a furcula (wishbone), and highly developed communication and navigation skills. All birds have their young by laying eggs.

The term *species* is often defined as a group of organisms that can reproduce naturally with one another and create fertile offspring. (*Note:* In this lesson, we refer to "kinds" of animals rather than *species*, as species is problematic to define for first graders. For instance, there are two species of ostrich and around 300 species of hummingbird, so it is much simpler to refer to an ostrich as a "kind" of bird.) Birds have common observable *traits*. In biology, traits are defined as specific characteristics of an organism. Adult birds of the same species have bodies and beaks that are similar in size and shape. Many birds exhibit sexual dimorphism, where two sexes of the same species have differences in size, color, markings, and so forth. For example, a male northern cardinal is brilliant red, whereas a female is pale brown with reddish tinges in the wings, tail, and crest.

It is fairly easy to identify the kinds of birds that commonly visit bird feeders. In this lesson, students observe feeder birds and try to identify the species based on observable characteristics. To do this, they use bird identification posters and/or an app from the Cornell Lab of Ornithology. Students quickly recognize the crosscutting concept (CCC) of patterns as they observe common traits and behaviors of bird species. They implement the science and engineering practice (SEP) of planning and carrying out investigations as they use their observations of birds to make comparisons and form ideas about bird

traits. They also use the SEP of asking questions as they share their wonderings about birds throughout the lesson.

Although species have common recognizable characteristics, there can be variations within each species. These variations are usually minor differences, such as a brighter yellow head on one male goldfinch compared with another or a wider black line around a cardinal's eye compared with another. These small differences can be difficult to observe on wild birds because it is hard to get an up-close look at fast-moving birds. Therefore, we include an article in the lesson explaining variations within a species. Here students use the SEP of obtaining, evaluating, and communicating information as they read the nonfiction article and discuss their learnings. This concept of variation of traits within a species is a foundational idea that students will build upon in later grades. In grades 3–5, students go more in-depth on the topic of inherited traits from parents to offspring, as well as how the environment can affect the traits an organism develops.

Learning Progressions

Below are the disciplinary core idea (DCI) grade band endpoints for grades K–2 and 3–5. These are provided to show how student understanding of the DCI in this lesson will progress in future grade levels.

DCI	Grades K–2	Grades 3–5
LS3.B: Variation of Traits	• Individuals of the same kind of plant or animal are recognizable as similar but can also vary in many ways.	• Different organisms vary in how the look and function because they have different inherited information. • The environment also affects the traits that an organism develops.

Source: Willard, T., ed. (2015). *The NSTA quick-reference guide to the* NGSS: *Elementary school.* Arlington, VA: NSTA Press.

engage

Ruby's Birds Read-Aloud

Connecting to the Common Core
Reading: Literature
KEY IDEAS AND DETAILS: 1.1

**Inferring**

Show students the cover of *Ruby's Birds. Ask*

? From looking at the cover, what do you think this book is about? (Answers will vary.)

Model how you can often find information about what a book is about by looking at the back cover. Read the paragraph on the back cover of the book that says, "Sometimes, an ordinary walk can become something … magical! Tag along with Ruby as she discovers that even big cities have a wild side."

Read the book aloud, then *ask*

? Where does Ruby's neighbor, Eva, take her? (Central Park)

? Why does Eva go to Central Park? (to look for birds)

? What does Ruby learn about how to behave when birdwatching? (Be silent. Be serious. Pay attention.)

? Why is that important? (If you are loud or moving around a lot, you will scare the birds away.)

? What kind of bird did Eva and Ruby find in Central Park? (a golden-winged warbler)

? Why was that particular bird special to Eva? (It is a bird that reminds her of her home in Costa Rica.)

Read the section on the "About This Story" page in the back of the book. Then show students a video of a golden-winged warbler singing (see the "Websites" section for the video link).

Ask

? What do you notice?

? What do you wonder?

Then *ask*

? Have you noticed different birds at school or at home? (Answers will vary.)

? What do they look like? (Answers will vary.)

? What do they sound like? (Answers will vary.)

? Where could we go to observe birds? (parks, forests, etc.)

? What could we do to attract birds to our schoolyard? (put up some bird feeders)

Set Up a Feeder Station

> **SEP: Planning and Carrying Out Investigations**
> Make observations (firsthand or from media to collect data that can be used to make comparisons.

Designate an area of the schoolyard as a bird feeder station (ideally outside a classroom window). You can purchase bird feeders, have students make them, or both. (See the "Websites" section at the end of this lesson for ideas and instructions for DIY bird feeders your students can make.) You may want to set up a baby monitor near the bird feeders and turn it on during appropriate times throughout the day so that students hear the sounds the birds

FEEDER STATION

make while visiting the feeders. Get your students involved in setting up your bird feeder station by asking questions such as the following:

? Where would be a good place at school to set up some bird feeders?

? Should we set them up on the playground where kids will be running around at recess? (No, we would scare the birds away.)

? Should we put them in the woods? (No, we wouldn't be able to see them.)

? What kinds of bird feeders should we include? (Answers will vary.)

Note: It is best for students to have experience observing the birds in their area, but if setting up a feeder station is not possible, the Cornell Lab of Ornithology has several live feeder cams you can use for this part of the lesson, or show students the PBS video "Who Comes to The Feeder?" (see the "Websites" section for these video links).

explore

Analyzing Bird ID Charts

> **Connecting to the Common Core**
> **Reading: Informational Text**
> CRAFT AND STRUCTURE: 1.5, 1.6

Print Bird Identification Charts that are customized to your area, such as the following (see the "Websites" section for how to access these charts):

- Project FeederWatch: Common Feeder Birds From Cornell Lab of Ornithology
- Celebrate Urban Birds
- Celebra las Aves Urbanas

> **SEP: Asking Questions and Defining Problems**
> Ask questions based on observations to find more information about the natural world.

Give each pair of students a bird ID chart and allow time to study it. As students observe the birds on the poster, *ask*

? What do you notice?

? What do you wonder?

Model some things you notice and wonder, such as the following:

- I *notice* that there many different colors of birds.
- I *notice* the title of the chart is …
- I *notice* that sometimes there are two of the same kind of bird next to each other with these little symbols: ♀♂.
- I *wonder* why some birds are brightly colored and others are dull.
- I *wonder* if these birds are also in our area.
- I *wonder* what the symbols mean.

Invite students to share their observations and wonderings. See if you can find some answers to your questions and theirs. For example, share that the ♀♂ symbols signify female and male. In many birds, the female and male have different sizes, colors, patterns, and so on. Explain that the birds on the chart are adult birds. Students may see some young birds that look similar to the adults but might be smaller, fluffier, or different colors. However, when the birds become adults, they will look very much like their parent birds.

Explain that these bird identification charts can help identify the birds that come to the classroom feeder. You may also want to use the free Merlin Bird ID app from Cornell Lab of Ornithology (see the "Websites" section). This user-friendly app asks students three simple questions to identify a bird:

? What was the size of the bird? (They click the picture that shows the relative size.)

? What were the main colors? (They can click from one to three colors.)

? What was the bird doing? (They can choose from eating at a feeder; swimming; sitting on the ground, in the trees or bushes, on a fence, or on a wire; or flying.)

The app creates a list of possible birds with photos, names, and even the sounds they make.

FeederWatch

When you have the feeders set up and students have studied the bird identification charts, it is time to watch the birds! Ask students to think back to the book *Ruby's Birds*, and *ask*

? What did Eva teach Ruby about how to behave when watching birds? (Be still, be quiet, and be serious.)

USING A BIRD ID CHART

Tell students that the author of *Ruby's Birds,* Mya Thompson, is an expert in observing nature. Read the following quote from Thompson:

"I've always loved to listen and watch. I was a shy kid, so observing was a big thing for me. All that observing got me really curious about the natural world. It led me to a career in biology and to Africa where I studied how elephants communicate with each other at pitches so low that humans can't hear them. In Ruby's Birds, I wanted to share how fun and exciting it is to learn how to watch and listen carefully because there are so many amazing things out there to see and hear once you know how to tune in. Observational skills are such a key part of science; I hope this book supports kids to channel their natural curiosity."

Take students outside to watch the birds. Remind them what they learned about bird watching from the book: "Be quiet, be still, and be serious." You may even want to set up a bird blind you can hide behind to watch the birds. Encourage students to use the charts and/or Merlin app when you are observing birds at your feeders. You may even have them take photos of the birds. Ask questions, such as the following:

? Do you notice any patterns about which birds visit which feeders or which birds are on the ground?

? How many of the same kind of bird do you see?

? Are the birds interacting with each other? If so, how?

? Can you identify any of the birds with the Bird ID Chart or the Merlin app?

> **CCC: Patterns**
> Patterns in the natural world can be observed, used to describe phenomena, and used as evidence.

Although students can learn many things about birds by watching them feed, the focus of this lesson is the idea that birds of the same species can be identified by common characteristics. So, when students identify a certain bird, *ask*

? How do you know that bird is a _____?

? What do all _____ have in common?

Students should use evidence from their bird chart or app to support their answers.

It is not important that students identify the birds correctly. Rather, they should have shared experiences observing wild birds and using the chart to notice similar characteristics.

explain

Birds of a Feather Article

> Connecting to the Common Core
> **Reading: Informational Text**
> CRAFT AND STRUCTURE: 1.4

> **SEP: Obtaining, Evaluating, and Communicating Information**
> Obtain information using various texts, text features, and other media that will be useful in answering a scientific question and/or supporting a scientific claim.

Give students an opportunity to share their observations and wonderings from the FeederWatch activity. *Ask*

? What patterns did you notice when watching the birds at the feeders? (Some birds were on the ground and others were on the feeders, birds stayed a short time and flew away, some birds visited the feeders in groups, and so on.)

? What characteristics do all birds have in common? (feathers, beaks, two feet, wings, and tails)

? In what ways were the birds different? (different colors, sizes, shapes, markings, actions, etc.)

? Were you able to identify any of the birds? (Answers will vary.)

? What are you wondering about birds? (Answers will vary.)

 *Features of Nonfiction*

Give each student a copy of the Birds of a Feather student page. Tell them that this article can help them learn more about the birds they observed. Explain that this is a nonfiction article, and that nonfiction sometimes has some different features than fiction. Project the article and discuss the following features of nonfiction before reading.

Title and Author

Point to the title and explain that nonfiction articles have a title at the top and often have the author's name listed. Sometimes, there is information on the author's job or schooling.

Columns

Explain that nonfiction articles are sometimes written in columns. Point out the two columns and explain that after the first column is read, you continue reading to the top of the second column.

Captions

Next, ask students to find the pictures. Explain that under the pictures, there are words that explain what is in the picture. These are called *captions*. Read the captions aloud for each picture.

Bold Print Words

Then ask students to look for any bold print words. Write the bold print words on the board: **traits, adult, flocks,** and **behaviors.** Explain that bold print is usually a sign that a word is an important vocabulary word. Tell students that as you read aloud, you would like them to follow along and try to determine the meaning of the bold print words.

Then read the article aloud. After reading, *ask*

? All birds are animals. But what makes a bird a bird? (Birds have wings, beaks, and feathers. Most birds can fly. All birds lay eggs.)

? From the reading, what do you think the word *traits* means? (characteristics, the way something looks)

? What are some examples of *traits* of birds? (size, color, type of beak)

? From the reading, what does the word *adult* mean? (grown-up)

? What is a *flock*? (a group of birds)

? What are some examples of different kinds of birds from the article? (ostrich, bee hummingbird, robin)

? What other kinds of birds have you seen or heard of? (Answers will vary.)

? From the reading, what is an animal *behavior*? (something that an animal does; the way an animal acts)

At the end of the article, students are asked to "spot the differences" in the two birds of the same kind and circle them. *Ask*

? What are the differences? (white patterns around the eyes, the white stripes on the wings, and the black tip on one of the beaks)

? What is the same about the two birds? (They have the same shape, size, dark-colored head, and so on.)

Explain that birds of the same species share the same main traits. They get these traits from their parent birds. Even though birds of the same kind look very much the same, there can be small differences between them. These differences are often hard to spot on wild birds like the ones that come to the feeders, because you can't get very close to the birds and because the birds are usually moving quickly.

elaborate

No Two Alike Read-Aloud

Show students the cover of *No Two Alike* and read the title. Then *ask*

? From looking at the cover, what do you think this book might be about? (Answers will vary.)

Read the book aloud. Then *ask*

? Now what do you think the book is about? (The two birds show examples of things that are similar but not exactly alike.)

? Do you think the two birds in the book are the same kind? (yes)

? Why? (They are the same size and shape. They have red bodies, black wings, stripes on their feet, etc.)

? How are the two birds different? (Their tails are different. One has black spots on the tip.)

Revisit the last page of the book that reads, "… but not quite" to show the two tail feathers and have students compare them.

Spot the Difference

evaluate

Spot the Difference Challenge

Give students the Spot the Difference Challenge student page. Tell them that they are going to color the two birds to be the same *kind* of bird but with a few small differences in *traits*. When they are finished with their birds, they will challenge the rest of their classmates to "spot the difference." Explain that in order to make it challenging, the differences in traits should not be *too* noticeable. Since the birds are supposed to be the same kind, they should be the same main color, have the same kind of feet, have the same shape and size of beak, and so on. The differences should be small. Students can choose a real bird to emulate or they can create an imaginary bird. As students are working, check in to make sure their two birds are mostly the same with just slight differences. When students are finished, they can challenge their classmates to "spot the difference!"

STEM Everywhere

Give students the STEM Everywhere student page as a way to involve their families and extend their learning. They can do the activity with an adult helper and share their results with the class. If students do not have access to the internet at home, you may choose to have them complete this activity at school.

Opportunities for Differentiated Instruction

This box lists questions and challenges related to the lesson that students may select to research, investigate, or innovate. Students may also use the questions as examples to help them generate their own questions. These questions can help you move your students from the teacher-directed investigation to engaging in the science and engineering practices in a more student-directed format.

Extra Support

For students who are struggling to meet the lesson objectives, provide a question and guide them in the process of collecting research or helping them design procedures or solutions.

Continued

Extensions

For students with high interest or who have already met the lesson objectives, have them choose a question (or pose their own question), conduct their own research, and design their own procedures or solutions.

After selecting one of the questions in this box or formulating their own questions, students can individually or collaboratively make predictions, design investigations or surveys to test their predictions, collect evidence, devise explanations, design solutions, or examine related resources. They can communicate their findings through a science notebook, at a poster session or gallery walk, or by producing a media project.

Research

Have students brainstorm researchable questions:

? Which kinds of birds can fly? Which kinds of birds can swim? Which kinds of birds can do both? Make a Venn diagram.

? Which kind of bird has the largest beak, heaviest weight, or widest wingspan? Which flies the fastest? Make a book of bird "super powers."

? What are some other foods birds eat besides seeds?

Investigate

Have students brainstorm testable questions to be solved through science or math:

? Do different feeders attract different kinds of birds?

? What kinds of birds and how many of them visit our feeders? Watch for 10 minutes for three days and report your results to celebrateurbanbirds.org.

? How do birds in other parts of the world compare to the birds in our schoolyard? Scan the QR code below or go to *www.allaboutbirds.org/cams to* check out the Bird Cams from Cornell Lab of Ornithology.

Innovate

Have students brainstorm problems to be solved through engineering:

? Can you design a bird feeder from recycled materials?

? Can you design a hummingbird feeder from recycled materials?

? Can you design a bird blind (a structure people can hide behind to observe birds so the birds don't know they are there)?

National Science Teaching Association

Websites

 Golden-Winged Warbler Sounds video
www.allaboutbirds.org/guide/Golden-winged_Warbler/sounds

 Project FeederWatch: Common Feeder Birds from Cornell Lab of Ornithology
https://feederwatch.org/learn/identifying-birds/#download-feederwatch-posters

 Celebrate Urban Birds
https://celebrateurbanbirds.org/wp-content/uploads/2016/11/BirdID-Guide_2016.pdf

 Celebra las Aves Urbanas
https://celebrateurbanbirds.org/wp-content/uploads/2017/11/BirdID-Guide_170918-NoMarks.pdf

 Live Bird Cams from Cornell Lab of Ornithology
www.allaboutbirds.org/cams

 Merlin Bird ID app from Cornell Lab of Ornithology
https://merlin.allaboutbirds.org

 Who Comes to the Feeder? video from PBS
www.pbslearningmedia.org/resource/evscps.sci.life.bio.feeder/who-comes-to-the-feeder

DIY Bird Feeders

 Full-Time Kid video on making a simple bird feeder
www.pbslearningmedia.org/resource/easy-diy-bird-feeders-full-time-kid/full-time-kid-birdfeeder

 Instructions for making a bird feeder from a milk carton
www.pbslearningmedia.org/resource/arct14.sci.zbird/bird-feeder

 7 DIY Recycled Bird Feeders from Earth911
https://earth911.com/home/7-diy-recycled-bird-feeders

More Books to Read

Lemniscates, C. 2019. *Birds.* Sommerville, MA: Candlewick Studio.
Summary: Simple, lyrical text and bold illustrations reveal the diversity of birds.

Matheson, C. 2019. *Bird watch.* New York: Greenwillow Books.
Summary: The reader must find bird species in the watercolor and collage illustrations. A nice introduction to birding.

Richmond, S. E. 2019. *Bird count.* Atlanta: Peachtree.
Summary: A young girl named Ava looks for birds around town as part of the Christmas Bird Count.

Reference

Barrowclough, G. F., J. Cracraft, J. Klicka, R. M. Zink. (2016). How many kinds of birds Are there and why does it matter? *PLoS ONE* 11(11): e0166307. *https://doi.org/10.1371/journal.pone.0166307.*

Birds of a Feather
By Karen Ansberry and Emily Morgan

What Is a Bird?
All birds are animals. But not all animals are birds! Birds have wings, beaks, and feathers. Most birds can fly. All birds lay eggs.

Different Kinds of Birds
Different kinds of birds have different **traits,** such as size, color, and type of beak. The size and shape of a bird's beak is a clue to what it eats.

The largest bird is the ostrich. It can grow to about 9 feet tall and weigh more than an **adult** human. An ostrich has a wide, flat beak. The smallest bird is the bee hummingbird. It grows to about 2 inches long and weighs less than a dime. A bee hummingbird has a long, pointy beak.

OSTRICH AND BEE HUMMINGBIRD TO SCALE

Birds of a Feather
Have you ever heard the saying "birds of a feather flock together"? It's true—birds of the same kind tend to stick together. You may have seen pairs, groups, or even large **flocks** of the same kind of bird.

Birds of the same kind have similar traits. For example, adult robins are all about the same size. They all have reddish-orange feathers on their breasts. They all have short beaks.

Birds of the same kind have similar **behaviors** too. You may have seen a robin hopping across a grassy lawn looking for worms. All robins hop. All robins sing. All robins gather twigs and grass for nest building.

ROBIN PULLING WORM

No Two (Exactly) Alike!
Birds of the same kind have similar traits, but no two birds are *exactly* alike. There can be small differences in traits. For example, the colors might be a little different or the pattern of white spots around the eyes might be a little different. Can you spot the differences in the robins below?

TWO ROBINS WITH SMALL DIFFERENCES

Spot the Difference Challenge

STEM Everywhere

Dear Families,

At school, we have been learning about **birds.** We learned that birds of the same kind have the same **traits,** but can have small differences. In other words, no two are *exactly* alike. To find out more, ask your learner the following questions and discuss their answers:

- What did you learn?

- What was your favorite part of the lesson?

- What are you still wondering?

At home, you can visit the Cornell Lab of Ornithology Bird Cam website to see LIVE footage of birds at feeding stations around the world.

 Scan the QR code or go to *www.allaboutbirds.org/cams* and visit some of the feeders. Choose one to write about below.

Where in the world is the feeder located? _____

You may want to type that location into a maps website or app to see how far it is from your home. Discuss how the birds compare with the birds around your home or school.

Draw a picture of one of the birds you observed.

National Science Teaching Association